THE SESAME STREET
TREASURY

Featuring Jim Henson's Sesame Street Muppets

VOLUME 11

STARRING
THE NUMBER
11
AND THE LETTER
R

Children's Television Workshop/Funk & Wagnalls, Inc.

WRITTEN BY:

Linda Bove with the
National Theatre of the Deaf
Michael Frith
Sharon Lerner
Jeffrey Moss
Norman Stiles
Ellen Weiss
Daniel Wilcox

ILLUSTRATED BY:

Tom Cooke
Mel Crawford
A. Delaney
Larry DiFiori
Mary Grace Eubank
Michael Frith
Harry McNaught
Joe Mathieu
Marc Nadel
Michael J. Smollin
Maggie Swanson

PHOTOGRAPHS BY:

John E. Barrett
Neil Selkirk
View-Master International Group

Manufactured in the United States of America   1 2 3 4 5 6 7 8 9 0
ISBN: 0-8343-0052-4 (set); 0-8343-0063-X (vol. 11)

Hey! You wanna play a remembering game? Well, play it anyway.

"Remembering" starts with an R, and so do all these nice words. Repeat after me:

One rat.

One rat, two rubber reptiles.

One rat, two rubber reptiles, three roomfuls of rusty radiators.

One rat, two rubber reptiles, three roomfuls of rusty radiators, four ragged, ripped, rumpled raincoats on the roof.

One rat, two rubber reptiles, three roomfuls of rusty radiators, four ragged, ripped, rumpled raincoats on the roof, five rude robbers throwing rotten radish rinds at a roaring, rampaging rhinoceros!

Got it? Good! Now, good riddance!

The Rescue

There is poor, poor Rapunzel. She
is trapped in that tower and can't get
down. She looks very, very SAD.

Now here I come! Doesn't
Rapunzel look HAPPY
to see me?

Rapunzel is letting down her
long, long hair. She is so
EXCITED!

I am climbing up to rescue her.
My, I feel so BRAVE.

Now I am letting Rapunzel down.
Oh, I feel so PROUD.

There goes Rapunzel. She is very HAPPY.
But now I am trapped in the tower.
I am so MAD I could squash a pea!

Where's Radar?

Big Bird is trying to find his teddy bear, Radar.
Radar is different from all the other teddy bears.
Can you find him?

Rr

Little Jack Horner
Sat in a corner,
Eating his Christmas pie.
He stuck in his thumb
And pulled out . . .
a RHINOCEROS!

Hickory, Dickory, Dock,
The RHINOCEROS
Ran up the clock.

There was an old woman
Who lived in a shoe.
She had so many
RHINOCEROSES
She didn't know what to do.

Sing a song of sixpence,
A pocket full of
RHINOCEROSES!

Old Mother Hubbard went
to the cupboard
To get her poor dog a bone.
But when she got there, she found . . .
a RHINOCEROS!

Ridiculous Rhinoceros Rhymes
may be silly, but RHINOCEROS
begins with the letter R, and
that's what's really important.

The Story of Princess Ruby

One day Princess Ruby was out in the garden painting a
picture of her Royal roses. Just as she was painting the last
rose petal, a fox jumped out from behind a rose bush.
Princess Ruby was so startled that she tripped over her chair
and fell right into the bucket of red paint. She had red paint
in her hair, red paint in her ears, and red paint all over her
Royal overalls. She was a mess.

"Blecch!" said Princess Ruby. "I will have to take a bath—and
I've already *had* one today! Oh, I *hate* the color red!"

Princess Ruby went upstairs to the Royal bathtub. Her
mother, Queen Rosalie, took the Royal scrub brush and began
to scrub the Princess. It took an hour to scrub the red paint
off her Royal face. It took another hour to scrub the red
paint out of her Royal hair. It took two more hours to scrub
the red paint out of her Royal ears. And worst of all, her favorite
pair of Royal overalls was ruined!

"Red, red, red! I *hate* the color red! I never want to see the color
red again! Mother," she said, "I want you to issue a Proclamation.
Tell *everyone* in the Kingdom to get rid of EVERYTHING that's red!"

Queen Rosalie, who always tried to please her daughter, said, "All right, dear. But are you sure that's what you want?"

"Absolutely!" shouted Princess Ruby. And so the Queen ordered everyone in the Kingdom to get rid of EVERYTHING that was red.

By now it was dinner time, and Princess Ruby was hungry. She went down to the Royal kitchen and spoke to the Royal cook.

"Royal Cook," she said, "I'm hungry. Make me my favorite sandwich—peanut butter and strawberry jam."

"I am so sorry, Your Highness," said the Royal cook, "but there is no strawberry jam. The Proclamation said we had to get rid of EVERYTHING red, and strawberry jam is red. So out it went! You will have to have peanut butter and mint jelly."

"Yucch!" said the Princess. "Mint jelly is green and disgusting. I *hate* mint jelly."

But that was all there was, so that was what she had.

After dinner it was time for the Princess to go to bed. "Royal Mommy," she said to Queen Rosalie, "will you please read me my favorite bedtime story?"

"Of course, dear," said the Queen. "Which one is that?"

"Oh," said Princess Ruby, "it's the one about the little girl who carries a basket of goodies through the woods to her grandmother's house."

"You mean 'Little Red Riding Hood'?" said the Queen. "We don't have that one any more. You wanted us to get rid of EVERYTHING red, so we had to throw it away. I'll have to read 'Little Boy Blue' instead."

"Aaaacch!" groaned the Princess. "I HATE that story!"

But that was all there was, so that was what she had.

The next day was Valentine's Day, Princess Ruby's favorite day of the year. She LOVED to get valentines. And since everyone in the Kingdom loved *her*, she always got a great many valentines. So, bright and early that morning, she ran down the path to meet the Royal mailman.

"Good morning, Royal Mailman," she said. "May I have my valentines, please?"

"Sorry, Princess," said the mailman, "but valentines are red, and the Proclamation said we had to get rid of EVERYTHING red. So I sent all the valentines to my aunt in Peoria. You'll have to go back and look at that Get Well card I brought you when you had the flu."

"That does it!" yelled the Princess. "Royal Mommy! Royal Mommy! Quick—we need another Proclamation."

"I thought we might," said the Queen, smiling. "I have one right here. I hereby proclaim that the color red is allowed back in the Kingdom!"

And right away, the mailman called his aunt in Peoria and she sent back ALL of Princess Ruby's valentines, AND a big jar of homemade strawberry jam, AND a brand-new copy of "Little Red Riding Hood." And that night, after Ruby had looked at all her valentines and eaten two big peanut butter and strawberry jam sandwiches, and Queen Rosalie had read "Little Red Riding Hood" to her twice, she looked up at her Royal Mommy and said, "Royal Mommy, I've really learned a lesson today. Red is a very important color. My favorite food has red in it, and my favorite story has red in it, and my favorite holiday wouldn't be the same without the color red. In fact, red is my favorite color. From now on I will wear only red overalls, and I will eat only red food, and I only want to hear stories about red things, and I want my room painted red. In fact, I want the whole palace painted red, and..."

Queen Rosalie leaned over, kissed her daughter on the forehead, and said softly, "Yes, dear. Go to sleep now, and we'll talk about it in the morning."

Ernie

Home:	123 Sesame Street
Favorite Food:	Peanut butter and jelly sandwiches
Favorite Drink:	Figgy fizz float
Best Friend:	Old buddy Bert
Favorite Activity:	Taking baths with Rubber Duckie
Favorite Book:	<u>True Bathtime Adventures</u>
Favorite Shoes:	Red sneakers
Favorite Wish:	To make Bert laugh
Favorite Saying:	"Rub-a-dub-dubby!"

Big Bird's Farm

PARTES DEL CUERPO
PARTS OF THE BODY

cabeza
head

pelo
hair

cuello
neck

brazos
arms

manos
hands

estómago
stomach

dedos de las manos
fingers

piernas
legs

pies
feet

dedos del pie
toes

Once Upon an Eleven

"Me, Cookie Monster, love cookies. Cookies are my life. When I find jar of cookies, it as good as finding pot of gold at end of rainbow. Just seeing cookies make me so happy! You know what make me even more happy? Eating cookies! Yum, yum. Crunch, crunch."

opposites

Things That Are Opposite

up

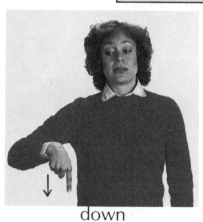

down

push

pull

in

out

big

little

over

under

hot

cold

old

young

Roosevelt Franklin, Doctor

COOKIE COUNTS 11

Hurrah for the number 11!
It really is 10 plus 1.
Eleven's the start of having
Some extra counting fun!

When you count to 10
On your fingers—
A handy thing to do—
Just wiggle one toe for 11
Or make just one tap
with your shoe!

Eleven's 1 less than a dozen.
Eleven's 1 more than 10.
Eleven's a nifty number.
Hurrah for 11 again!

Cookie Monster's Shape Cookies

COOKIES GRATIA COO...KIET

Salutations! *(That mean "Hi, there!")*

Me back for DELICIOUS page of COOKIE making. This time me show you how to make different-SHAPED cookies. O.K.? This one pretty tricky.

First, take some cookie dough out of icebox. If you all *out* of cookie dough (oh dear!) just make some more!

Sprinkle cloth with flour and put dough on cloth. Roll dough out flat, about ¼ inch thick. Now come the tricky part—need to find things to make SHAPES with. Let me see ... Ah! Can use GLASS to make round cookies ... and those box lids make good rectangles and squares.

Me just push them down on dough and peel away dough on outside.

First me make circles ...

Then me make squares and rectangles.

But how me make triangle?

Aha! Good idea! Me cut square in half, like this!

Me make TWO triangles.

Now me heat oven to 400 degrees, put cookies on ungreased cookie sheet, and put cookie sheet in oven. Have a grownup help you with the oven! O.K., now come hard part again. Me have to wait six to eight minutes while cookies cook. What me going to eat? Furniture all gone....

REMEMBER! Never use oven without grown-up helping you.

Wait a minute! Did me say PAGE was delicious? Me try—YUM ... pretty good. (It nice rectangle, too.)

Big Bird wonders: Why do people wear clothes?

Why do people wear clothes?
People wear clothes to keep warm.
Clothes can keep people from
getting wet in the rain.
People also wear clothes because
they like to be covered up.
Clothes make people look nice.
But I'm a bird!
Birds don't need clothes! Why not?
My feathers keep me warm and dry.
My feathers cover up my skin.
My feathers look very, very nice!
If people had feathers like me,
they wouldn't need clothes!

King Marvin the Magnificent was very grand indeed.
He said, "I am magnificent." His subjects all agreed.
"King Marvin is magnificent! Our kingdom is most blest.
Of all the Kings who ever were, King Marvin is the best."

Now in King Marvin's kingdom lived a little boy named Paul
Whose favorite thing was playing with a bright pink rubber ball.
He bounced his rubber ball all day against the palace gate.
He started in the morning and he stayed till it grew late.

One day as he was playing ball, he stopped and said, "I know!
I think I'll throw my rubber ball as high as it will go."
So Paul wound up and threw the ball with one tremendous fling.
"Oh, no!" he cried. "It's headed for the window of the King!"

Smash! went the royal window,
   and before the King could duck,
The ball bounced off
   King Marvin's throne . . .

      and hit his nose . . .

         and stuck.

"What *is* this thing?" said Marvin
    as he felt the ball and sneered.
But before he could remove it,
    his Prime Minister appeared.

"King Marv!" cried the Prime Minister.
    "A rubber ball! How cute!
    It really is magnificent! I'll get one for *my* snoot."

And like a flash he left the room, and what do you suppose?
When he returned, a rubber ball was stuck upon *his* nose.

The news spread quickly through the land
(the kingdom was quite small).
Soon on each person's nose there was
a bright pink rubber ball.

The butcher and the baker and the driver of the bus
All said, "If Marvin likes it, then it's good enough for us."

"Don't we look great!" the people cried.
    "Our noses are so pleasing!
Except it's rather hard to smell, and even harder sneezing."

But everyone was happy, the whole kingdom filled with joy,
For everybody had a ball—except for one small boy.

"Oh, woe," cried Paul, "without my ball
        I really am so sad.
I'll ask the King to give it back—
        I hope he won't be mad."

Paul tiptoed to the throne room
    where King Marvin was alone.
The King in his magnificence
    sat on his royal throne.

Young Paul knelt down before the King
    and then was told to rise,
But when he lifted up his head
    a strange sight met his eyes.
King Marvin wore an ermine cloak,
    silk slippers on his toes,
A golden crown was on his head . . .
    and a ball was on his nose.

Then Paul began to giggle, and he laughed till he was sore,
And pretty soon he laughed so hard, he fell down on the floor.

"What's so funny?" said King Marvin,
    as he saw that Paul was staring.
"It's your nose!" cried Paul with laughter.
    "That's my favorite toy you're wearing."

"My nose looks great!" King Marvin said.
Said Paul, "I beg to differ.
You really do look silly
with that ball stuck on your sniffer."

"I do?" exclaimed King Marvin.
"Bring my royal mirror quick."
King Marvin looked. He saw himself,
and what he said was..."Ick!"

"I really do look silly,
and I knew it from the first.
I've always said that rubber balls
on noses are the worst!"

The King took off the rubber ball and handed it to Paul.
"You've taught me a great lesson,
    so I'll give you back your ball."
Then the butcher and the baker and the driver of the bus
Said, "If Marvin gave his ball away...
            that's good enough for us!"

The people of the kingdom gave their rubber balls away
And they all have worn their noses plain...
            ... right to this very day.

So from early in the morning time until it grows quite late,
Paul has a hundred balls to bounce against the palace gate.

Now this story has a moral
And it's very, very true—
If a king does something silly
You don't have to do it too.

Ernie and Bert Present...
Shape Pictures

Ernie,
I have the square,
the triangle, and
the rectangle. All
you had to get
was the circle.

How can we
make shape pictures
if you don't have
the circle?

Bert and Ernie
are proud to present
SHAPE PICTURES!

Here are some
pictures we made out of these
shapes... And here are some extra
shapes for YOU to make
pictures out of. That triangle
might make a *nifty* pigeon...

Hey, Berd... cad I hab
by dose bag dow?

Rodeo Rosie's Ranch

Find the things that begin with the letter R.

RAIN

Rain, rain, go away,
Come again another day;
Little Johnny wants to play.